One Pink Sari

One pink sari for a pretty girl,
Two dancing women all in a whirl,
Three charmed cobras rising from a basket,
Four fat rubies, in the Rajah's casket,
Five water carriers straight and tall,
Six wicked vultures sitting on the wall,
Seven fierce tigers hiding in the grass,
Eight elephants rolling in a warm mud bath,
Nine green parrots in the coconut tree,
Ten twinkling stars, a-twinkling at me!

Ann Marie Linden

10

11

Miss Antrobus

Why do you love your octopus,
Miss Antrobus, Miss Antrobus?
Why do you love your octopus,
Miss Antrobus, my dear?

I love my octopus because
It hugs me and it wriggles.
I love my octopus because
Its wriggles give me giggles.
I love my octopus because
It juggles jars of pickles.
I love my octopus because
It tickles, oh, it tickles.

Richard Edwards

12

Serenade

Three mice sat down
in the barn one day
in a quiet corner
filled with hay.

One played a fiddle.
One played a drum.
One blew a bubble
with pink bubble gum.

Tra-la-la went the fiddle.
Boom, boom went the drum.
And POP! went the bubble
and the bubble gum.

Bobbi Katz

13

Little Pippa

Pip Pip Pippety Pip
Slid on the lino
Slippety Slip
Fell downstairs
Trippety Trip
Tore her knickers
Rippety Rip
Started to cry
Drippety Drip
Poor little Pippa
Pippety Pip.

Spike Milligan

Slippety slip

Trippety trip

Rippety rip

Drippety Drip

Adam Adam

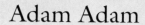

Adam Adam lost his shoe,
Mary Mary lost hers too,
Sara Sara found another,
Gave it to her baby brother,
Baby brother chewed the leather,
Baby sick, now all together;
Shoes shoes not for eating,
Shoes for putting smelly feet in.

Petonelle Archer

Zing! Whizz! Ping!

Zing, whizz, ping,
Goes the popcorn in the pan.
Zing, whizz, ping,
Try and catch me, if you can.
Zing, whizz, ping,
Watch me hopping in the air.
Zing, whizz, ping,
You can eat me, if you dare.
But I'll make your tummy sing
With a zing, whizz, ping!

Cynthia Rider

Sugarcake Bubble

Sugarcake, sugarcake
  Bubbling in a pot
Bubble, bubble sugarcake
  Bubble thick and hot.

Sugarcake, sugarcake
  Spice and coconut
Sweet and sticky
  Brown and gooey.

I could eat the lot.

Grace Nichols　　27

The Meal

Timothy Tompkins had turnips and tea.
The turnips were tiny.
He ate at least three.
And then, for dessert,
He had onions and ice.
He like them so much
That he ordered it twice.
He had two cups of ketchup,
A prune, and a pickle.
'Delicious,' said Timothy.
'Well worth a nickel.'
He folded his napkin
And hastened to add,
'It's one of the loveliest breakfasts I've had.'

Karla Kuskin

Something in my Soup

'What's that in my soup, Mummy?'
'Oh no, it's the baby's dummy!'

Charles Thomson

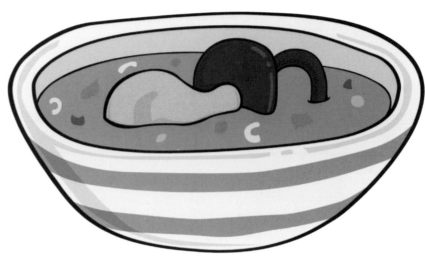

Cabbage

Sometimes Grandma gives me things
I do not like to eat,
Cabbage leaves with soggy strings
And slimy luncheon meat.
I push them round and round the plate
And when she isn't looking
I stuff into my wellingtons
The worst of Grandma's cooking.

Jean Willis

29

There Was an Old Lady

There was an old lady
    Whose kitchen was bare,
So she called for the cat
    Saying, 'Time for some air!'

She sent him to buy her
    A packet of cheese.
But the cat hurried back
    With a basket of bees.

She sent him to buy her
    A gallon of juice.
But the cat reappeared
    With a galloping goose.

She sent him to buy her
    A dinner of beef.
But the cat scampered home
    With an Indian chief.

She sent him to buy her
　A bowl of ice cream.
But the cat skated in
　With a whole hockey team.

She sent him to buy her
　A bite of spaghetti.
But the cat strutted up
　With a bride and confetti.

She sent him to buy her
　A fine cup of tea.
But the cat waddled back
　With a dinosaur's knee.

The fridge was soon bulging,
　And so was the shelf.
So she sent for a hot dog
　And ate it herself.

Dennis Lee

31

Down at the Dinosaur Fair

You can turn,
you can twist
in the prehistoric mist,
feel the dampness in your hair.
You can sprint,
you can spin
from a big bony chin
    down at the Dinosaur Fair!

You can swoop,
you can swing
from a dark leather wing
and fly through pillows of air.
You can slip,
you can slide
on a scaly scarlet hide
    down at the Dinosaur Fair!

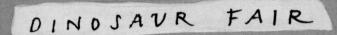

DINOSAUR FAIR

You can zing,
you can zoom
down a backbone flume,
whizz round in a waltzing chair.
You can whip,
you can whack
on a slippy saddle back
  down at the Dinosaur Fair!

You can trip,
you can trek
up a narrow bendy neck
any day, any time, any where.
You can flail,
you can float
like a wave-tossed boat
  down at the Dinosaur Fair!

John Rice

The Castle

There's a castle under the table in the lounge
With bats and owls;
Its walls may look like cardboard
And its doors like bathroom towels,
But that is just a trick to fool the dragons' beady eyes
For the castle under the table in the lounge
Is in disguise.

There's a castle under the table in the lounge
With one dark cell
Where every day my wizard, Wex,
Invents a different spell.
Today it's one to turn invaders slowly into stone;
There's a castle under the table in the lounge:
Leave it alone!

There's a castle under the table in the lounge
With steps that go
Through miles of smoky nothingness
To secret caves below
Where blacksmiths forge intruder-traps that snap with teeth of tin;
There's a castle under the table in the lounge:
You can't come in!

There's a castle under the table in the lounge
With seven towers
Where seven fair princesses sing
To seven lutes for hours,
And seven servants guard their doors with seven snarling hounds;
There's a castle under the table in the lounge;
It's out of bounds!

There's a castle under the table in the lounge
In which I hide
While dragons calling, 'Tea-time! Tea-time!'
Lumber by outside—
As if I'd fall for that one, no, I'm staying here all day,
In my castle under the table in the lounge,
So keep away!

Richard Edwards

39

Yuck!

Jam all over her fingers,
pastry in her hair,
fruit juice dribbling down her chin
and custard everywhere.

Playdough in her fingernails,
mud between her toes,
and something much, much nastier
running from her nose.

But none of that would bother me,
if it weren't for this:
my sister's heading this way fast
and it's *me* she wants to kiss.

Paul Rogers

42

My Baby Sister

My baby sister's
really swell.
I love her smile
but not her smell.

Bruce Lansky

43

Today's My Birthday

Today's my birthday.
Now I'm four.
I'm one year older
Than I was before.

I measured myself
Against the wall
And I'm over a hundred
Centimetres tall—

Much taller than
I used to be,
When I was small
And only three.

Today's my birthday.
Now I'm four.
I'm older and bigger
Than I was before.

John Foster

46

Birthdays

If birthdays happened once a week
Instead of once a year,
Think of all the gifts you'd get
And all the songs you'd hear,
And think how quickly you'd grow up;
Wouldn't it feel queer
If birthdays happened once a week
Instead of once a year?

Mary Ann Hoberman

On Being Five

I am five and it's my birthday
Bounce, bounce, bounce.
I won't wear my party dress
Flounce, flounce, flounce.

Cakes and crisps are on the table
Jelly and ice-cream.
Sara wants to eat it now
Scream, scream, scream.

It's my birthday, it's my birthday,
Streamers in the hall.
It's my party, it's my party,
Mummy up the wall.

I am five and I've got presents
I want more.
George has spread the chocolate icing
On the floor.

Daddy thinks the clown is funny
So does Aunty Sue,
Amy thinks the clown is scary
Boo hoo hoo!

Bradley won the pass the parcel
It's not fair,
It's *my* birthday, *I* get presents,
Pull his hair.

It's my birthday, what a party!
When I'm six years old
I've promised everyone I will be
Good as gold.

Petonelle Archer

49

Accidental ABC

A is for Accidents
(Spilling my food)
It's *splat* on the floor
And now Mum's in a mood.

B is for Bruises
(on *both* of my knees)
Mum says it's my fault
For climbing up trees.

But C is for Cuddles
(Mum holding me tight)
When monsters and bears
Come for me in the night.

Lucy Coats

52

Wizard Bear

If you trap your fingers in the door,
Or fall and bang your knee on the floor,
Who's always there to cuddle and care?
Wizard Bear.

If you hear a noise during the night,
Have a bad dream and wake with a fright,
Who's always there to cuddle and care?
Wizard Bear.

If you're full of cold, lying in bed,
With a runny nose and aching head,
Who's always there to cuddle and care?
Wizard Bear.

If you're down in the dumps, feeling sad,
If you've done something naughty and bad,
Who's always there to cuddle and care?
Wizard Bear.

John Foster

53

Mama, Papa, and Baby Joe

Under over Coca-Cola
Off to Pick 'n' Pay we go,
Moany moany macaroni,
Mama, Papa, and Baby Joe.

Harum-scarum through the traffic
Ziggery-zaggery park the car.
Bumpity-bump along the pavement
Around the block and there you are!

In an out the shops so busy
Mama and Papa go yackety-yack.
See you later, escalator
Okey-dokey, clickety-clack …

54

Spaghetti falling pitter-pat,
Hot and bothered screaming Mama
'DON'T DO THAT!' **'DON'T DO
THAT!'**

Checkout lady checks the shopping
Money honey jingle jam,
Papa, Mama in a tizzy
Boogie-woogie in the pram! ...

In Fatty Boom Boom's Take Away,
Sticky icky licking baby
Mama smiling, it's OK! ...

Shopping packed and home we go!
Honky-tonky through the city
Mama, Papa, and sleepy Joe.

Niki Daly

55

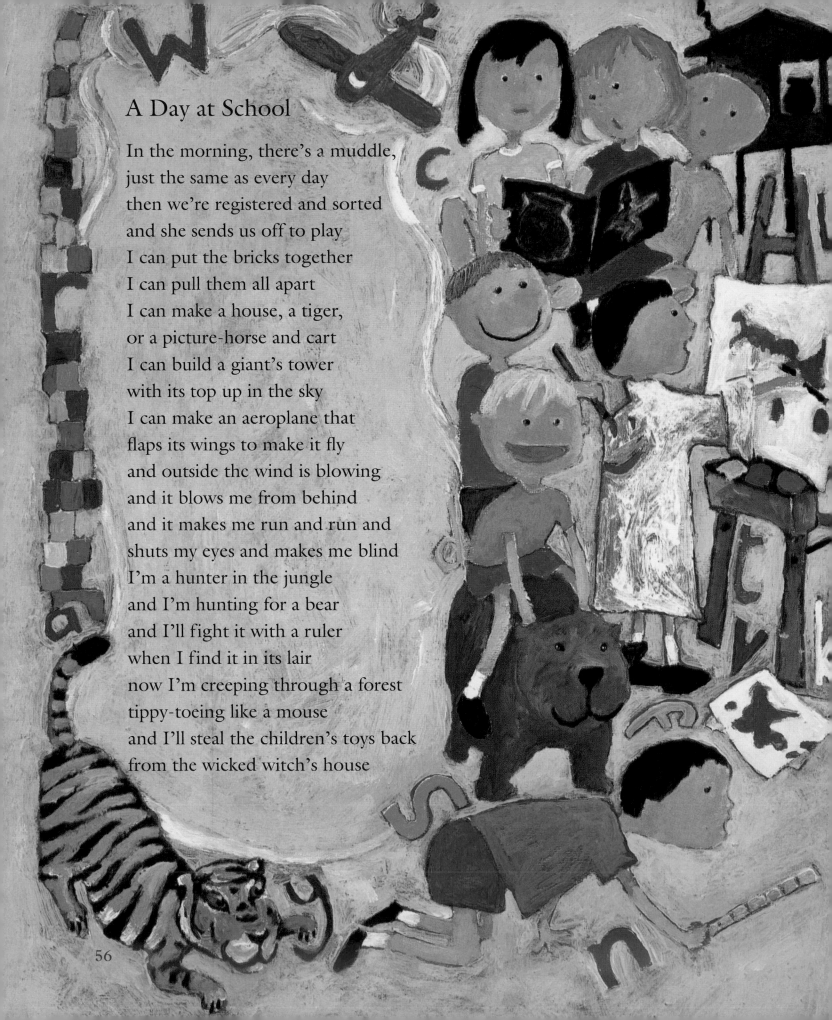

A Day at School

In the morning, there's a muddle,
just the same as every day
then we're registered and sorted
and she sends us off to play
I can put the bricks together
I can pull them all apart
I can make a house, a tiger,
or a picture-horse and cart
I can build a giant's tower
with its top up in the sky
I can make an aeroplane that
flaps its wings to make it fly
and outside the wind is blowing
and it blows me from behind
and it makes me run and run and
shuts my eyes and makes me blind
I'm a hunter in the jungle
and I'm hunting for a bear
and I'll fight it with a ruler
when I find it in its lair
now I'm creeping through a forest
tippy-toeing like a mouse
and I'll steal the children's toys back
from the wicked witch's house

56

now it's in-time and the bell rings
story-time now on the mat
with the alphabet in colour
and the cat who wears a hat
now we're back inside the classroom
and the big ones do their sums
but we're little so we're playing
and we're playing Dads and Mums
I don't want to be a Daddy
I'm a creepy slimy thing
with a hundred legs and whiskers
and a great big purple STING!

Jessie Thomas

57

Cats

One cat, two cats, three cats, four,
Four cats scratching
At my gran's back door.

Five cats, six cats, seven cats, eight,
Eight cats scratching
At my grandma's gate.

Eight cats, seven cats, six cats, five,
Five cats scratching
At the old bee-hive.

Four cats, three cats, two cats, one,
One cat napping
In the noon-day sun.

John Kitching

There was a young girl called Maggie

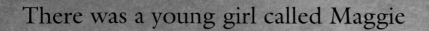

There was a young girl called Maggie
Whose dog was enormous and shaggy.
  The front end of him
    Looked vicious and grim—
But the tail end was friendly and waggy.

Anon.

Puppy

Here is our puppy, a black and white romper,
A bustler, a bouncer, a champion jumper;
A racer, a chaser, who never stops saying,
It's great being a puppy, it's all barking and playing.

Jack Ousbey

Watching a Bumble Bee

Out in the garden
   you will see
the oh-so-busy
   bumble bee.

It never stops to
   take a rest.
It wears an oh-so-hairy
   vest.

When flowers, in summer,
   open wide
the bee dives oh-so-deep
   inside.

It gathers nectar
   all day long,
and hums an oh-so-buzzy
   song.

While you watch from your
   garden seat
the bee makes honey
   oh-so-sweet.

Then off it zigzags
   in a tizz
with an oh-so-busy
   buzzy
     whizz zzzzzzzzzzzzzzzz

Wes Magee

Caterpillar

Creepy crawly caterpillar
Looping up and down,
Furry tufts of hair upon
Your back of golden brown.

You will soon be wrapped in silk,
Asleep for many a day;
And then, a handsome butterfly,
You'll stretch and fly away.

Mary Dawson

The Garden Path

The garden path at Grandma's
Leads past the little pond,
Where nimble golden fishes hide,
To tunnelled leaves beyond.

And through the jungly bit you find
A gate beside a tree,
And a huge world made of grass and sky
A far as you can see.

Shirley Hughes

Pony

Clip-clop, swing along,
Swish-a-tail, neigh,
Pony in the meadow
Is up and away;
Frolicking and frisking,
As if to say,
It's a kick-a-leg, shake-a-mane,
Swish-a-tail day.

Jack Ousbey

Feeding Ducks with Grandad

When Grandad takes us to the park
We always take some bread,
He says before we have some fun
The ducks must all be fed.

And when the ducks have all been fed,
Too full to flap their wings,
Then Grandad races really fast
To beat us to the swings.

Coral Rumble

At the Park

At the park
I like to have:

a diving fling
on a flying swing,

a quick funnel
through a dark tunnel,

a slippery glide
down a shooting slide,

and a whirling flier
on a twirling tyre.

But best of all:

is being dizzily wound about
on a busily spinning roundabout!

Ian Souter

71

In August

When the sun is strong
    And the day is hot,
We move around
    At a peaceful trot.

We don't wear much
    In the way of clothes
And we squirt ourselves
    With a garden hose.

Marchette Chute

74

Seaside

Sand in the sandwiches,
   Sand in the tea,
Flat, wet sand running
   Down to the sea.
Pools full of seaweed,
   Shells and stones,
Damp bathing-suits
   And ice-cream cones.

Waves pouring in
   To a sand-castle moat.
Mend the defences!
   Now we're afloat!
Water's for splashing,
   Sand is for play,
A day by the sea
   Is the best kind of day.

Shirley Hughes

A Winter Parcel

Today I'm like a parcel,
wrapped up from top to toe,
protected from the icy winds,
the rain, the sleet, the snow.

My head has got a hat on,
my neck hides in a scarf,
and on my hands are puppet gloves,
a tiger and giraffe.

My coat is thick and furry,
and does up very high,
and on my feet I've special boots,
to keep me warm and dry.

So though there's little of me
that anyone can see,
this walking, talking parcel is
most definitely ME!

Linda Hammond

Knitting

Our budgie's wearing bootees,
our puppy's wearing mittens,
there's a warm scarf on our cat,
and cardies on our kittens,
our goldfish wears a beanie
though I fear it doesn't fit,
and all because my grandma
loves to sit and knit and knit.

Nigel Gray

79

Winter Morning

It's sleeting, it's snowing,
a north wind is blowing,
my ears are red,
my fingers feel dead,
and my cherry-red nose is glowing.

Nigel Gray

Doctor Foster

Doctor Foster went to Gloucester
On a winter's day.
An icicle froze
On the end of his nose
And it didn't fall off till May.

Richard Edwards

80

Galoshes

Susie's galoshes
Make splishes and sploshes
And slooshes and sloshes
As Susie steps slowly
Along in the slush.

They stamp and they tramp
On the ice and concrete,
They get stuck in the muck and the mud;
But Susie likes much best to hear

The slippery slush
As it slooshes and sloshes
And splishes and sploshes
All round her galoshes!

Rhoda Bacmeister

81

Bedtime, Teddytime

It's bedtime, it's teddytime,
it's pyjamas at the readytime.

It's bedtime, it's tunetime,
it's watch the milky moontime.

It's bedtime, it's blisstime,
it's one more goodnight kisstime.

John Rice

Cubby

Grandma has a lion cub
With worn-out ears and fur,
It once belonged to a little boy
Who used to live with her.
That little boy was my father,
It gives me such a thrill
To think that his kisses and cuddles
Are stuck to the lion cub still.

Jean Willis

82

Wee Willie Winkie

Wee Willie Winkie runs through the town,
upstairs and downstairs in his nightgown,
the wind's very chilly—he's shivering like a jelly:
are the children in their beds?

No, they're watching telly!

Nigel Gray

83

Bedtime Song

The stars above are glittering
The moon is gleaming bright
And noisy cats are singing songs
Down in the yard tonight
MIAOW WOW WOW
WOW WOW

People in their dressing-gowns
In houses far and near
Are leaning from their window sills
They're horrified to hear
MIAOW WOW WOW
WOW WOW

But we don't want a lullaby
We prefer a din
Noisy cats are what we like—
All join in!
MIAOW WOW WOW
WOW WOW
WOW WOW

Quentin Blake

Nighty Night

Nighty night
Sleepy tight,
Don't let those buggies bite.
If they bite
(And some of them do)
Smack their behinds
With the sole of your shoe.

Lucy Coats

Index of titles and first lines

First lines are shown in *italics*

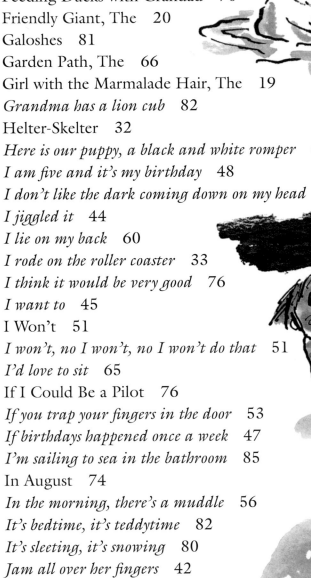

Lullaby

The stars have switched their lights on.
Day's curtains have been drawn.
The birds are resting in the trees.
There's dew upon the lawn.

The toys are in their boxes.
The stories have been read.
It's time for drifting off to sleep
Tucked safely up in bed.

John Foster